Book 1

By John Holzmann
Illustrated by Dave Lilly

Published by
Avyx, Inc.
8032 South Grant Way
Littleton, CO 80122-2705
(303) 483-0140 FAX (303) 483-0141
E-Mail: info@avyx.com

ISBN 978-1-887840-49-1

CPSIA facility code: BP 312991

Table of Contents

* By Duane Bolin

"The more that you read,

the more things you will know,

the more that you learn,

the more places you'll go."

— Dr. Seuss

Pat

Pat is a rat.

Pat is fat.

Pat is a fat rat.

The fat rat is Pat.

Is Pat fat?

Pat is fat.

Pat is Fat Rat Pat.

is   a   the

Nat

Nat is a cat.

Nat is fat.

Nat is a fat cat.

That fat cat is Nat.

Is Nat fat?

Nat is fat.

That cat is Fat Cat Nat.

<u>t</u>hat

A Mat and a Hat

Pat the rat is on a mat.

Is the mat *his* mat?

Pat is on his mat.

A hat is on Pat.

Is the hat *his* hat?

The hat on Pat is his hat.

Fat Rat Pat has a mat and a hat.

on   his   has

A Cat on a Hat

Fat Cat Nat is on a mat.

Nat is on the mat

that Pat the rat is on.

Nat sat on a hat

on the mat.

Is that the hat on Pat?

Nat sat on the hat

that is on Pat!

A Flat Hat

Fat Cat Nat

sat on a hat.

The hat is on Pat the rat.

Is the hat Nat sat on flat?

The hat *is* flat!

The hat on Pat is flat. $\longrightarrow$

Is *Pat* flat?

Pat is flat!

Nat sat and sat

on Pat and the hat.

Nat! Scat!

Nat sat and sat.

Nat is Bad

Fat Cat Nat is on a hat.

The hat is on Pat

the fat rat.

The hat is flat and Pat is flat.

Pat is flat, Pat is sad,

and Pat is mad!

Nat is a bad cat!

Can Pat Tap Nat?

Nat sat and sat on the hat
and on Pat.

Pat is mad and Pat is sad.

Can Pat tap Nat?

Tap Nat, Pat!

Tap that Nat!

Tap! Tap! Tap!

Nat is Sad

Pat can tap Nat.

Tap! Tap! Tap!

Is Nat glad?

Nat is *not* glad. Nat is sad!

Bad Nat is sad! $\longrightarrow$

not

9

And Pat?

Pat is glad.

Nat ran!

Nat ran and ran.

*****

The hat on Pat is not flat.

And Pat is not flat.

Ham, Jam, and a Yam

Ann has a ham, jam

and a yam.

Is the ham that Ann has bad?

The ham Ann has is not bad.

Is the yam bad?

The yam is not bad.

And the jam? . . .

Bad Jam

Is the jam Ann has bad?

That jam *is* bad!

Ann has bad jam.

And the bad jam is

on the ham.

The bad jam is on the ham.

Bad jam on a ham!

That is bad!

The ham is bad.

And Ann is not glad.

Ann is sad.

Jan, Nan, and Matt

Jan has a nag.

Matt has a ram.

Nan has a cab.

said   he

Matt said, "Sam the ram

can pass Val the nag."

Jan said, "He can not!

Val the nag can pass

Sam the ram!"

Nan said, "Hal the cab is fast.

Hal can pass Val and Sam."

Sam, Val, and Hal Ran

Sam the ram, Val the nag,

and Hal the cab ran.

Val and Hal pass Sam.

Val and Hal lap Sam.

Hal laps Val as Val laps Sam.

Hal the cab laps and laps

Val the nag.

Hal the cab laps and laps and *laps*

Sam the ram!

A Bad Fan

As Hal laps Val, his fan taps!

Hal can not pass!

Hal's fan is bad!

The fan taps and taps!

Hal can not pass Val the nag.

Hal can not pass Sam the ram.

Nan raps Hal's fan.

Nan is sad.

Val Laps the Cab

Hal the cab sat.

Val the nag ran.

And Sam the ram ran.

Can Val pass Hal?

Val can! Val can pass the cab.

Val laps the cab.

Val laps and laps Sam the ram.

to

Val the nag is fat.

Val has to nap.

"Val!" said Jan. "Not a nap!"

Val sat and had a nap.

And as Val had a nap, Sam ran.

Can Sam Win?

Hal the cab sat.

Val the nag had a nap.

Sam the ram ran.

Sam ran and ran.

Can Sam pass Hal? Sam can!

Nan is sad

as Sam laps the cab.

"Bad cab!" Nan said.

"Jan!" said Nan. "Tap Val.

win

Val can not nap."

Jan taps Val. Val naps.

Can Sam pass the nag

as Val naps? Sam can!

Sam laps Val!

And Sam wins!

A Pig Pit

Dad said to Tim,

"The land in the pig pit is bad.

Go dip sand in it.

"And," said Dad, "do not go

in the pit! Lil will be mad.

Lil has a kid pig. And a pig

that has a kid will nip."

go   do   I   be

Tim said,

"I will go and dip sand in the pit."

Tim ran to the pig pit.

The Kid Pig

Lil the pig is fat.

Lil sits on a hill in the pig pit.

A kid pig is at Lil's hip.

Tim dips sand in the pit.

The kid pig dips his lip

in the sand and sips it in.

"Quit it!" said Tim.

"Sand is not to sip!"

"Yip!" said the kid pig,

and bit the sand!

In the Pit

The kid pig bit the sand

and did not quit.

"Quit it!" said Tim.

"The sand is not to fill a pig!

The sand is to fill the land."

The kid pig still did not quit.

Tim is mad.

Tim ran into the pit.

Lil ran to Tim

and bit him on his hip!

At that, Dad ran in.

"Lil!" said Dad. "Quit!"

Dad

"Dad!" said Tim.

"Lil bit me!

Lil is a bad pig!"

"Tim!" said Dad.

"I said do not go in the pit!"

"The kid is bad!" said Tim.

"He bit the sand and did not quit."

me   he   <u>s</u>he

"Tim!" said Dad.

"I said Lil has a kid.

And if a pig has a kid,

she will do as Lil did.

Tim is bad. And I am sad."

Was Tim Bad?

"If a pig has a kid,

she will ram and nip," said Dad.

"She will rip and jab.

She will kill if she can. . . ."

"It is bad to kill," said Tim.

Dad said, "It is bad to go in the

pit if I said do not go in the pit."

we   was

Dad was sad Tim ran into the pit.

He was sad Lil bit Tim.

He was glad Lil did not kill Tim.

"I did bad," said Tim.

"I did not do as Dad said.

It was bad to go in the pig pit.

It was bad to hit Lil."

"Can we go fix that hip?"

said Dad.

My Dog

My dog is big.

He can sit.

He can dig.

My dog can be bad.

He can yap.

He can jab.

my   dog

My dog can be sad.

He will yip

if I am sad.

My dog will wag

And bat my hand

if I am glad.

A Rat Zaps a Nap

Bill's dad has a nap.

He has a nap on the hill.

He has that nap till Bill taps him.

Bill quips, "Dad! Dad! We have

a rat in a can of jam at the mill!"

have of no

Bill's dad has no wits and asks,

"We have a *hat*

in a *pan of sand* at the mill?"

"No, Dad!" said Bill.

"I said, 'A *rat* is in a

can of jam at the mill!' "

Bill's dad did not gab.

He and Bill ran to the mill.

A Cat and a Rat Scat

Bill and his dad ran to the mill.

"The rat will not go," said Bill.

"I have a lid on the can

the rat is in."

At the mill, a cat sits

on the lid of the can.

Bill's dad wags his

hand at the cat. The cat scats.

Bill's dad taps the can

the rat is in.

The rat has had his fill of jam.

The rat scats.

"Bill," said Dad, "tag the can

Bad Jam."

Bill said, "I will!"

Pals

Dan and Jim are dads.

Dan has six lads.

Dan's lads are

Al, Cal, Hal, Tim, Bill, and Tad.

Jim has no lads. Jim has gals.

Jim's gals are Jan,

Sal, Jill and Kim.

are	says	for

Dan's lads and Jim's gals are pals.

As the pals gab, Al says, "Dad and Jim have ribs!"

"Pass the ribs!" Jan says to the dads.

"No," says Dan. "The dads have dibs on the ribs."

"No ribs for kids," says Jim.

Ribs and Dip

The lads and the gals are mad.

"No ribs for kids!?"

"We have crab dip," Cal

says to the dads. "If we pass

the dip, will you pass the ribs?"

"Pass the ribs, Jim!" says Dan.

"Pass the dip," says Jim

to the kids.

you

The dads pass the ribs

as the kids pass the dip.

Tad spills ribs on his lap.

Tad is sad.

Jim hands Tad a rib bib.

Tad wags the bib and grabs a rib.

Tad is glad!

A Big Bug

Kip is at the Bug Lab.

Jim jabs a bag at him.

"Kip, pin and tag

the bug in this bag,"

he says. "I can not."

why

"Why not?" asks Kip.

"I am mad at that bug," says Jim.

"Why?" says Kip.

"That bug bugs me!" says Jim.

"Why?" says Kip.

"That bug is bad," says Jim.

The Big Bill Bug

Jim says, "This bug is bad."

Kip says, "Why is the bug bad?"

*****

This man runs up, says Jim.

He has a big bug in his hand.

As he runs up, the bug jabs him
in his hand.

The man yips, and the bug

flaps up, up, up.

We can not grab it.

The man says, "Can you pin

and tag that bug?

If you do, I will pass you

six big bills.[1]"

[1] six big bills = six hundred-dollar bills

Jim Nabs the Bug

The bug lands on my hat,

says Jim.

The hat is on my lap.

I grab a cup.

I slam it on the bug.

The bug is in the cup.

I tip the bug into a bag so I can

pin and tag the bug at the lab.

so

I run to the bus stand.

But as I run, I trip.

I stand up and the

bus is at the stand.

But as I run, the bus runs on!

So I am not on the bus!

The Bus Trip

Jim says: I sit at the bus stand.

I have a cut lip.

A bus comes.

The bus man says

I do not have the bill I must have.

I can not go on the bus.

come/comes   get

"Fix the bill," he says,

"and you can go in a bit."

I fix the bill and sit at the bus

stand. A bus putts up. $\longrightarrow$

The bus man says,

"This bus has a bad cam.

That is why it putts.

I can not have you come

on my bus."

And so I sit a bit.

A bus comes. Can I go on it?

The bus man says I can.

So I get on.

I Can Not Win

The bus runs

till it hits the hill, says Jim.

But the hill has a big, bad

jam on it.

A bus has hit a van.

A cab has hit the bus.

And a big rig has hit the cab. $\longrightarrow$

say

"I have to be at the lab!"

I say to the bus man.

"But I can not go

if we have a jam!"

says the bus man.

"We have to sit

till the jam is past."

54

So we sit.

Do I come to the lab in a jiff?

No, I do not! I can not win.

"That *is* a bad trip," says Kip.

"But why do I have to pin
and tag the bug?"

"I am sick of it," says Jim.

Kip says he will pin
and tag the bug.

Bud and Jud

This is Bud. Bud is a fox.

Bud is big. Bud is bad.

Bud is a big, bad fox.

This is Jud. Jud is a fox.

Jud is thin. Jud is mad.

Jud is a thin, mad fox.

fox

Jud and Bud are pals.

Bud and Jud are bad,

mad fox pals.

Bud and Jud hiss.

Jud and Bud fuss.

Bud and Jud are bad,

mad fox pals full of sass.

Pigs and Foxes

Jill, Lil, and Babs are pig pals.

Foxes and pigs are not pals.

Bud and Jud plan to nab the pigs

as a snack.

"The foxes have a plan

to have us as a snack,"

says Jill to Lil and Babs.

"We can run!" says Babs.

Babs, Lil, and Jill ran

and hid in a sand pit.

Fox Plans

Bud and Jud had a plan

to have a snack of pigs.

But the pigs ran and hid

in a sand pit.

The foxes are mad.

Bud gabs at Jud.

Jud yaps at Bud.

The foxes yip and yap

till Bud says, "Can we plan an

attack? A bit of wit and the pigs

will be ham!"

"Ham!" says Jud.

"Yum!" says Bud.

Jud grabs a map and

the foxes run to the pit.

A Dud!

Back at the pit,

the pigs fill bags with sand.

At last, Jill, Lil, and Babs

have a big sand bag hut.

with

The foxes are glum,

but the pigs are glad.

The foxes sit and plan.

And the pigs nap.

Bud says, "We can zap the pigs."

Bud and Jud mix gas

and mud in a tub. $\longrightarrow$

The mix fizzes.

Jud dips a can in the tub

and flips it at the hut.

No bam. No buzz.

The mix is a dud!

A Huff and a Puff

The foxes' mix of gas

and mud is a dud.

The pigs' hut still stands.

Jill, Lil, and Babs are glad. $\longrightarrow$

does   give

Bud and Jud are mad.

"I have a plan!" says Jud.

"We will kick the hut

and huff and puff. It will tip . . .

and we will have ham!"

Bud huffs. Jud puffs.

The foxes kick the hut.

But the hut still stands.

The hut does not tip.

The foxes have no ham.

The foxes give up.

The pigs win!

Eggs

Jen has a yen

for ducks and hens.

She has a hen. She has a duck.

But the hen and the duck

can not have eggs.

| or | from |

And with no eggs, a duck or

a hen can have no kids.

So Jen gets six duck eggs and

ten hen eggs from the egg man.

She is glad!

The Eggs Rest

Jen's hen has a nest in a hen hut.

The hen can not sit on ten eggs.

So Jen sets six eggs in a pan.

The pan with the eggs

has grass in it.

A lamp on the pan acts as a hen.

The hen sits on the rest of the eggs.

The duck sits on the duck eggs.

The duck's nest is in the grass.

She hid it in a pit in the grass.

The duck eggs and the hen eggs

rest in the nests and in the pan.

Chicks!

The lamp eggs crack.

The lamp has chicks!

The hen's eggs crack.

The hen has chicks!

And Jen has ten chicks.

The chicks say, "Pip, pip!"

chick

Jen says the chicks are Flip, Hip,
Lip, Mip, Nip, Pip, Quip, Rip,
Sip, and Tip.

The chicks peck the grass.

The chicks nip bugs.

The chicks sip drips.

The chicks have fluff.

"This is fun," says Jen.

And she grins.

Ducks!

The duck's eggs crack.

The duck has six ducks!

No. She had six eggs.

But she has a chick

and the rest are ducks!

The duck sat on a hen egg!

The ducks say, "Quack, quack!"

The chick says, "Pip, pip!"

Jen says the ducks are Mack,

Pack, Quack, Sack and Tack.

She says the chick is Bip.

The ducks peck at the grass.

A pup comes and sniffs the ducks.

The pup yaps.

The ducks jump and quack.

And Bip says, "Pip, pip!"

The ducks nip at the pup.

The pup runs off.

Jen says, "It is grand to have a
mess of ducks and chicks!"

Ducks and a Chick

Mack, Pack, Quack, Sack, Tack

and Bip go on a trip.

They go to swim.

Mack, Pack, Quack, Sack and

Tack jump in.

They swim. They dunk.

They nip at bugs. $\longrightarrow$

they

But Bip is left to stand.

Chicks do not get wet.

And so he says a sad "Pip, pip!"

Jen comes and gets Bip.

She hands Bip to the hen.

The hen will have

ten chicks plus Bip.

Bip will be glad.

Pals' Pets

Ben and Ken are lads.

They are pals.

Ben runs and Ken runs.

Ben has a fat cat. The cat is Sid.

Sid sits in the sun.

He naps on his red rug.

Ken's pet is a hen, Jen.

She clucks at Ken. $\longrightarrow$

them   then

Ken says, "Ben. Let's grab a
bug net and tin with a lid.
Let's get bugs for Jen."

The pals get ten bugs for Jen.

Ken gives the bugs to Jen.

She snaps them up. (Yum!)

Then she rests in her hen den.

Pals Run

As the pets rest, Ben and Ken gab. Then Ben jumps up and tags Ken. "You are it!" he says and runs.

"I am not!" says Ken. And he runs and tags Ben. →

The lads tag and run till Ben
trips. When Ken tags him,
Ben says, "The sun is so bad.
I quit."

"The sun *is* bad," says Ken.
"But let's not quit. Let's swim
and get wet."

"I will be glad to swim," says
Ben. "That will be fun."

And so the pals go for a swim.

Cut Lip

Ben and Ken have a snack.

They have ham on buns.

Ben hands the ham can to Sid.

Sid licks the lid. (Yum!) But then

he cuts his lip on a bit of tin.

Ben and Ken run to the vet
with Sid. $\longrightarrow$

"Can you fix Sid?" asks Ben.

The vet mends Sid's lip.

The vet dabs wax on the cut.

"The wax will fix Sid's cut," says the vet.

The vet pats Sid.

Sid is on the mend.

Ben is glad and so is Sid.

Add a Pet

Ben's mom has said no to a pup in the past. "A cat is grand," she said. "But I do not have the bucks for a pup."

But a man gives Ben bucks to dig land for him.

Ben has dug a lot of land for the man, so he has ten bucks. $\longrightarrow$

Ben asks his mom, "Can I get
a pup?"
"I do not have the bucks to get a
pup," she says. "Do you?"
"Yes," says Ben. "I have
ten bucks."

Ben's mom taps her desk.

"If you can get a pup for

ten bucks," she says, "Then,

yes. A pup will be fun."

Ben hugs his mom.

She hugs him back.

Add a Pup

Ben and Ken go to pick a pup.

The pals go to Ted's Pet Den.

Ted has lots of pups—

fat and thin pups,

red, black and tan pups.

The pups are glad and sad

and mad.

| <u>thin</u> | one |

Ben has just ten bucks to spend.
And just one pup is ten bucks or
less. That pup is Rex.

Rex wags and sits.

Ben pets Rex.

Rex licks Ben's hand.

Rex jumps and licks Ken's lips.

The lads grin.

$\longrightarrow$

Ben gets Rex.

Rex runs to kiss Mom with licks.
Mom grins. "You have a grand
pup," she says to Ben.

I *Did* Read It!

This Certificate of Completion
is hereby granted to

JACOB Kim EmiLY

to certify completion of

I Can Read It!
Book 1

Ms. Kim
_____
Presented by

11·12·14
_____
Date